Goal!

Written by Jane Langford

Illustrated by James Browne

Alex wanted to be a footballer.
It was his dream.

Every day, he kicked his ball up and down the garden.

He kicked the ball between
the plant pots.
"Goal!" he shouted.

There was a football team at
Alex's school.
"Who wants to play in the team?"
asked Mr Barnes.

Alex put up his hand.

"I want to play!" he said.

"How old are you?" said Mr Barnes.

"Six," said Alex.

"You have to be seven to play in the team," said Mr Barnes. Alex was very upset.

He stopped kicking his ball
up and down the garden.
He stopped shouting, "Goal!"

"What's the matter, Alex?"
asked Mum.

"I'm too young to play football,"
said Alex.
"Who says?" asked Mum.

"Mr Barnes says you have to be seven to play in the team," said Alex.
"But you can still play football," said Mum.

"No, I can't. I'm too young
to play in the team," Alex said.
Then he kicked the mat.

"What month is it?" said Mum.

"April," said Alex.

"When is your birthday?"

"May," said Alex.

"That's not long. Let's count how long it is."

Alex's birthday was in sixteen days. "Less than three weeks!" said Alex. "Yes," said Mum.

"And then I can be in the team?"

"Yes," said Mum.

Alex ran to get his ball.

He kicked the ball between the plant pots.
"GOAL!"
he shouted.